EDGE

NO. 8

TABLE OF CONTENTS

SIGIL
Chapters 27 & 28
Hundreds of years of war come down to a death match between Samandahl Rey and Khyradon, the Lizard God.

SCION
Chapter 28
Kort ascends the Raven throne as Ethan and Ashleigh struggle to maintain Sanctuary Isle.

WAY OF THE RAT
Chapter 5
Boon and Po Po flee from assassins and run straight into the Khan!

MYSTIC
Chapter 26
Giselle's tour of the magical world of Ciress takes her to the Shaman Guild, where she must face her deepest fear.

RUSE
Chapter 11
The untold tale of how a strange and powerful artifact turned Simon and Lightbourne into bitter enemies.

THE FIRST
Chapters 21 & 22
Pyrem flies off to rescue Ingra, leader of House Sinister, and we learn the strange life story of the ruthless Seahn.

now hear this

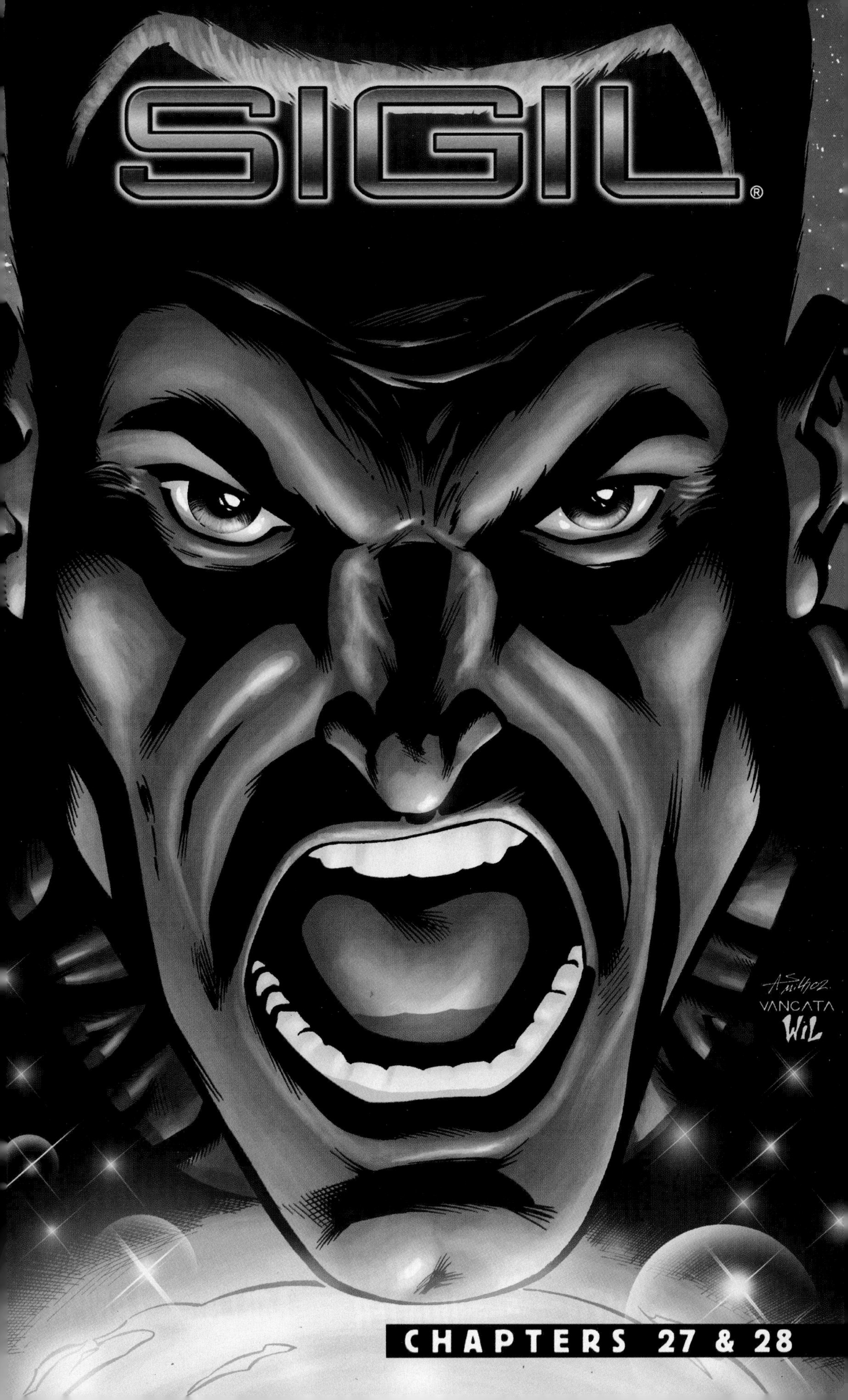
SIGIL®
VANCATA
WiL
CHAPTERS 27 & 28

OUR STORY SO FAR...

SAM

ROIYA

JeMERIK

ZANNIATI

TCHLUSARUD

KHYRADON

FOR CENTURIES, the five human worlds of the Planetary Union have been at war with the lizardlike Saurians of Tcharun, unable to find a weapon formidable enough to turn the tide of battle. And then along came Sam.

A mustered-out soldier with a good heart, SAMANDAHL REY and his fellow ex-soldier ROIYA SINTOR came looking for work on the neutral world Tanipal only to be ambushed by Sam's Saurian enemy TCHLUSARUD. In the ensuing battle, they picked up two crucial allies – the mysterious JeMERIK MEER (smitten by Roiya) and ZANNI (a spy anxious to escape the harem of Tanipal's Sultan). Victory, though, came not from any of them but rather from a strange sigil, a brand of vast power burned into Sam's chest by a vanishing stranger. In fact, Sam first realized the sigil's potential when Roiya was slain – and Sam, in a moment of anguished grief, neutralized the attack by unintentionally unleashing a half-mile-wide explosion of matter-transforming force.

Once Sam, JeMerik and Zanni escaped Tanipal, however, an over-wrought Sam learned that all was not lost; while Roiya's lifeless body lay in stasis aboard Sam's starship, the *BitterLuck*, her mind and soul had been "uploaded" into the ship's computers seconds before her death, allowing Roiya to live on in holographic form. Now the two of them are taking point in defending the human race from the merciless Saurian army, with Sam on one side as the Planetary Union Field Commander and Khyradon, a self-styled war god, leading the Saurians in an all-out attack on the Union.

PREVIOUSLY...

The Planetary Union prepares for all-out war against the Saurians led by Sam and the crew of the *Bitterluck*. But seismic scans of Gaia reveal that the asteroid strikes to the planet's surface have created a tectonic crisis that threatens the very structure of the world. The Saurians may already have struck the deathblow before the retaliatory force has even left the Gaian system.

Zanni, Roiya, JeMerik and a host of Planetary Marines invade the Saurian homeworld of Tcharun where a civil war rages; a war that threatens to annihilate them no matter which side claims victory. At the same time, Sam rushes back in an attempt to save Gaia, the central world of the human race.

Chuck **DIXON**
WRITER

Andy **SMITH**
PENCILER

Brad **VANCATA**
(CHAPTER 27)
& Rob **HUNTER**
(CHAPTER 28)
INKERS

Matt **MILLA**
COLORIST

Dave **LANPHEAR**
LETTERER

"DO YOU THINK HE CAN SAVE *GAIA?*"

"WHY DO YOU ALWAYS ASK ME QUESTIONS YOU KNOW THE ANSWERS TO?"

"DO *YOU* THINK HE CAN SAVE GAIA?"

"HE *HAS* TO."

"IF IT'S *POSSIBLE* THEN HE'S THE *ONLY* ONE WHO CAN DO IT.

"HE COULD HAVE *PASSED* ON THIS."

"HE WAS *COMMANDED* AWAY FROM HERE BY THE PRESIDENT HERSELF."

"MAYBE YOU *DON'T* KNOW EVERYTHING, SMART GUY."

BRING UP A *PULSE CANNON!*

UNTIL WE CAN BRING DOWN THE TEMPLE DOORS, THIS IS A *FORLORN* HOPE!

TCHLUSARUD! WE *HAVE* NO HEAVY GUNS LEFT!

THEN WE MUST FIND *ANOTHER* WAY IN, KCHASKCHA!

HOW? KHYRADON'S ZEALOTS ARE *SLAUGHTERING* MY WARRIORS!

A *SHIP.*

ALL *THREE* GODS ABANDON US.

OUR AIRSHIPS HAVE BEEN DESTROYED.

"PERHAPS *NOT,* KCHASKCHA--"

-- FORTUNE WORKS ON A PATH *UNKNOWN* TO US.

LOSER?

"WHICH SIDE IS *HE* ON?"

NOW THE UNION NEEDS **ONE** MORE SERVICE FROM YOU.

GO TO TCHARUN AND **END** THE REIGN OF THE MONSTER KHYRADON.

BEFORE HE CAN STRIKE AT US AGAIN

HOW *LONG* UNTIL WE REACH THE SAURIAN FRONTIER, ADMIRAL?

SOON *ENOUGH*, COMMANDER REY.

I HAVE A UNIT THAT *MAY* BE IN A BAD WAY.

IF THEY'RE IN *LIZARD* SPACE, THEN I ASSURE YOU--

ROIYA!

NOT SURE HOW LONG I CAN *HOLD* THIS CONTACT, SAM--

KHYRADON *ISN'T* ON TCHARUN--

UNNH?

WHERE *IS* HE?

WE HAVE NO WAY OF *KNOWING*.

HOW CAN I *FIND* HIM?

THAT'S UP TO YOU--

--MAYBE YOUR VANISHING ACT--

I'M NOT *SURE* HOW THIS WORKS BUT HERE I GO.

REY? WHAT'S *HAPPENING*?

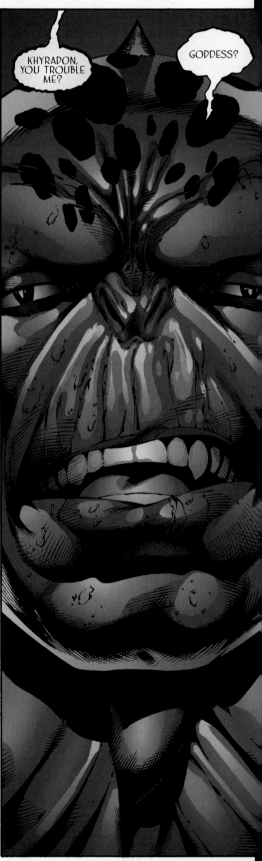

NO!

I CAN'T LET THIS *HAPPEN*--

--I *ALREADY* SAVED GAIA TWICE.

→UNH←

--COME *ON*, REY--

--YOU--

→UH←

--*WEAK*-KNEED--

--SONOVA--

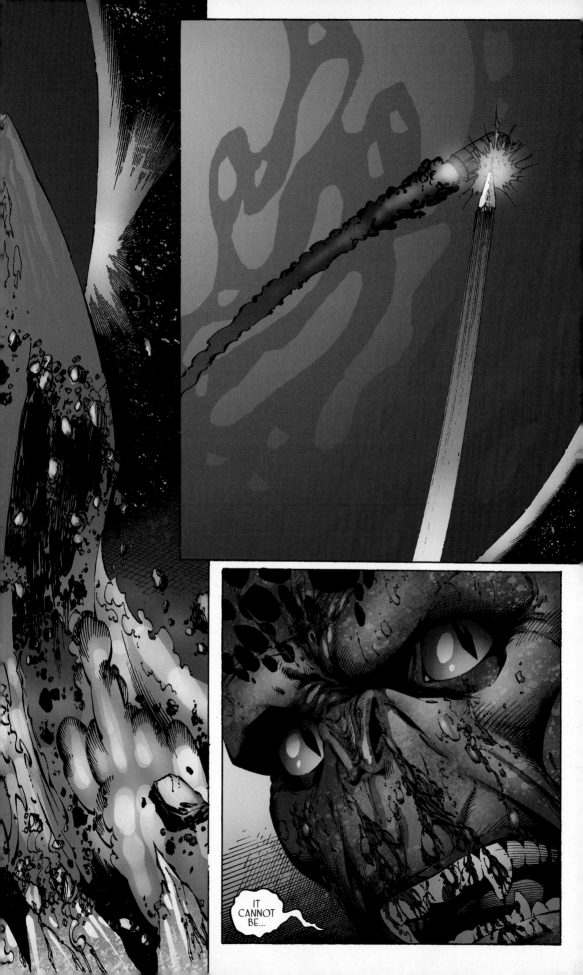

IT
CANNOT
BE...

CHAPTER 28

Thus Far in Scion

hat started with a mysterious sigil led to war. Prince Ethan of the West-ruling Heron Dynasty was graced with a mark granting him power, leading to the accidental scarring of Prince Bron of the East-ruling Raven Dynasty during ritual combat.

War between the kingdoms followed, but as the conflict raged, Ethan pledged his loyalty to the Underground movement dedicated to freeing the genetically engineered Lesser Races. His companion in this was Ashleigh, Raven princess and sister to Bron. Eventually the two gave in to their mutual attraction and became lovers.

Ethan and a small band of followers, including his sidekick Skink, the bounty hunter Exeter, and Nadia, a traveler from the far kingdom of Tigris, took control of the Tournament Isle. The island, located in the Great Sea between Raven and Heron lands, became a sanctuary for the Lesser Races. When the fleets of both kingdoms converged on the Isle, Ethan used his power to end their conflict and apparently slay Bron.

Now Ethan and Ashleigh face the challenges of maintaining their newly-founded kingdom.

Ron Marz WRITER

Jim Fern Guest PENCILER

Don Hillsman II INKER

Jason Keith COLORIST

Troy Peteri LETTERER

"...BUT I WOULD HAVE MY *CORONATION* REMEMBERED."

The war is over.

The great conflict the kingdoms of the Ravens and the Herons wage upon one another has ended...

...brought to a sudden conclusion by the same man who started it.

Ethan, youngest of the Heron princes, sparked the war with an unintended slight against Raven Prince Bron in the tournament of combat contested by the kingdoms.

Ethan drew an end to the war, here where it began, by literally forcing the Ravens and Herons to lay down their arms. It also seems he slew his rival Bron.

Now Ethan has taken this island that was used for combat and made it a sanctuary.

Here, finally, the Lesser Races can live as the free beings they should be.

There's a certain irony that Ethan's companion in all this has been Bron's sister, the Princess Ashleigh.

Having broken with their respective kingdoms, they've become lovers...

...and are attempting to lead this new kingdom of theirs, a scrap surrounded by the vastness of the Great Sea.

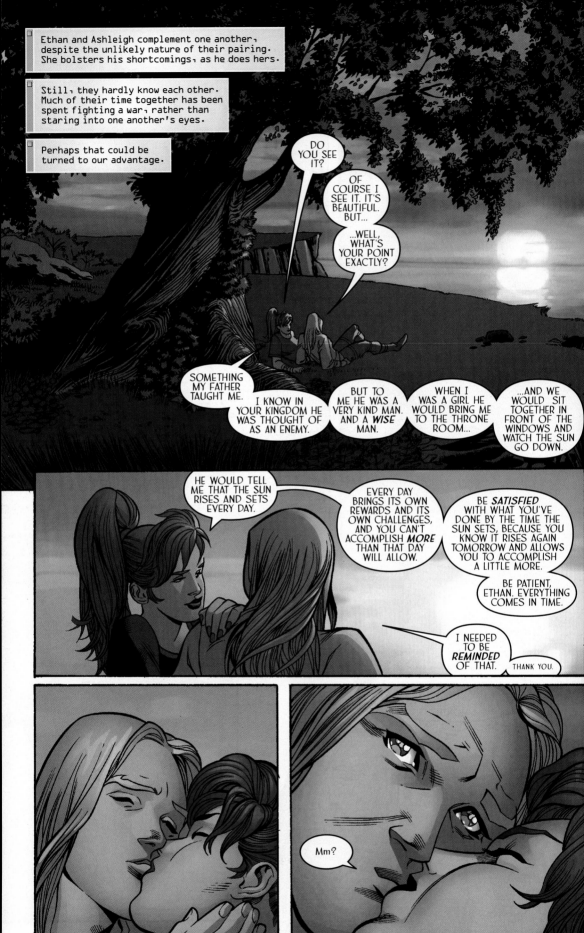

...and he is truly formidable.

Though she is not blessed with the power that he is, Ashleigh is easily as capable.

She will stand at his side. Always.

They are to be reckoned with, both of them...

AGH!

THERE ARE *TOO MANY!*

...but so, too, are they young and inexperienced.

AHHN!

GHH!

Best, they are idealistic. They could be led to see the way of things.

Especially if it was presented to them by someone they have come to trust and consider a friend.

ETHAN...

...ASHLEIGH...

Someone who has, at times, even been their savior.

WE'RE FORTUNATE YOU HAPPENED ALONG WHEN YOU DID. THANK YOU, NADIA.

I'M HAPPY TO SERVE.

TRUTHFULLY, I WAS ONLY LOOKING FOR A PLACE TO ENJOY THE SUNSET MYSELF.

I'M ALWAYS HESITANT TO DISTURB THE TWO OF YOU. YOU MUST NOT GET ENOUGH PRIVACY AS IT IS.

WHY *DID* YOU HAPPEN ALONG, NADIA?

NO.

WE *DON'T* GET ENOUGH PRIVACY.

IT'S HARD. THERE'S ALWAYS SO MUCH THAT HAS TO BE DONE FOR THE ISLAND, THERE'S NEVER ANY TIME LEFT FOR *US*.

MAYBE YOU'RE RIGHT, ASHLEIGH. MAYBE I *SHOULD* LEARN A LITTLE PATIENCE.

SINCE IT'S NEARLY IMPOSSIBLE FOR US TO SPEND TIME TOGETHER *HERE*...

...AND SINCE I THINK NADIA AND EXETER CAN HANDLE THE ISLAND FOR A FEW DAYS...

...WHAT WOULD YOU THINK ABOUT GOING TO THE HERON LANDS TO VISIT MY *FAMILY?*

I was sent here to look for weakness.

We'd hoped these kingdoms would decimate one another and make themselves easy prey. They've stopped short of that. But I believe we've found powerful allies who already believe in our cause. Very soon we'll bring them into the fold.

And then this world will be ours.

DID YOU FORESEE THIS, MARIELLA?

I MEAN *TRULY?*

DID I KNOW ETHAN WOULD LEAVE US? I SUSPECTED.

A MOTHER HAS A *SENSE.* HE WAS ALWAYS DIFFERENT THAN OUR OTHER CHILDREN, AND NOT SIMPLY BECAUSE HE WAS THE YOUNGEST.

BUT EVEN *I* COULDN'T HAVE IMAGINED THIS DESTINY. ETHAN SET ASIDE HIS HERITAGE FOR ANOTHER CAUSE...

...AND YET I CAN'T BE TERRIBLY DISPLEASED. HE'S ACCOMPLISHED GREAT THINGS.

ETHAN'S CHOSEN A DIFFICULT PATH FOR HIMSELF. I PRAY HE'S EQUAL TO THE CHALLENGES AHEAD OF HIM.

I TOLD HIM I WAS *PROUD* OF HIM, MARIELLA, AND I AM. PERHAPS EVEN MORE SO THAN IF HE'D REMAINED HERE.

HELLO?

IS SOMEONE THERE?

IF SOMEONE'S THERE...

...SHOW YOURSELF.

CHAPTER 5

The frontier city of Zhumar, last outpost of the Empire where civilization and barbarism clash. All caravan roads lead here. Every wild tribe covets its treasures.

Boon Sai Hong is a common thief who calls this mountain stronghold home. On one regrettable night in his criminal career he stole two ancient artifacts from an old librarian; the Ring of Staffs, which gives its wearer instant mastery over any staffed weapon, and the Book of the Hell of The Hungry Dragons, a scroll depicting the damned souls devoured by the worms of the afterlife.

Now Boon is a hunted man trapped in a walled city isolated in a thousand miles of frozen wilderness. He is pursued by Judge X'ain, appointed by the Emperor to be the unquestioned overlord of Zhumar. The Thieves' Guild also wants Boon's head for violating the oath given to their brotherhood to share and share alike. Princess Zheng Mai Lo, daughter of the Emperor, also seeks the Ring and the Book and another artifact not stolen by Boon: the fabled Phoenix Heart. The Silken Ghost, a mysterious lady warrior, is also shadowing Boon for reasons unknown.

The Khan's attack on the city begins in earnest now. His hordes of archers and swordsmen harry the walls even as the great cannon known as the Mouth of God threatens to reduce Zhumar to rubble...

Chuck **DIXON**
WRITER

Rod **WHIGHAM**
guest PENCILER

Drew **GERACI**
guest INKER

Chris **GARCIA**
COLORIST

Dave **LANPHEAR**
LETTERER

"WINTER HAS SO LONG BEEN OUR *ALLY*, CLOAKING US FROM THE DANGERS WITHOUT.

"FOR A FEW FROZEN MONTHS WE WERE *SAFE* FROM HARM.

"BUT WITH THIS SEASON'S SNOW CAME THE *HORSEMEN*."

"To my enemies I say,
May you live in
interesting times."

Wing Tei Sun

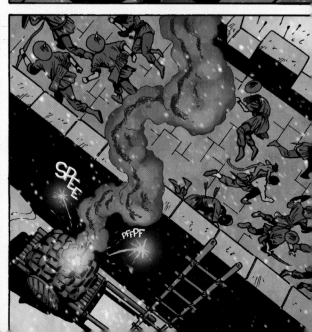

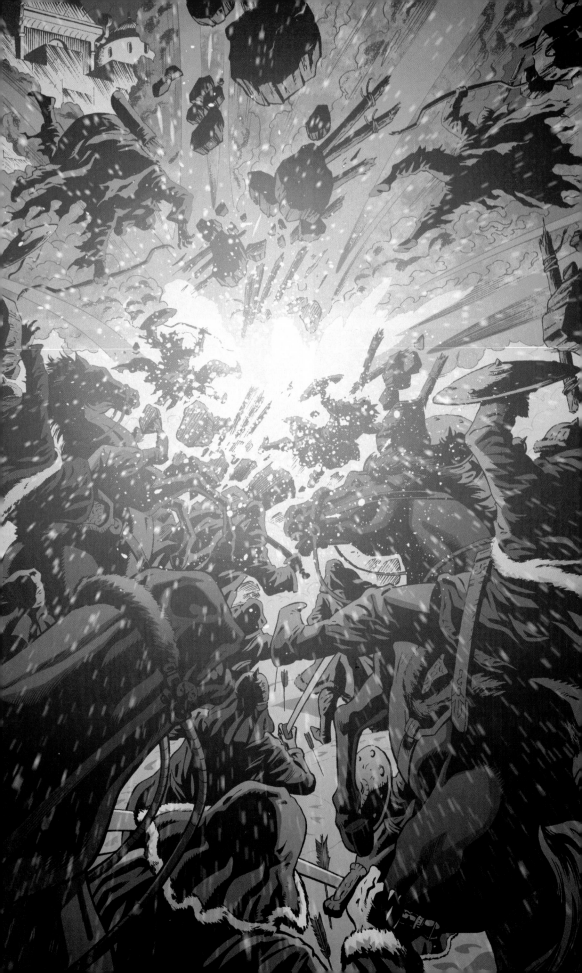

MYSTIC™

CHAPTER 26

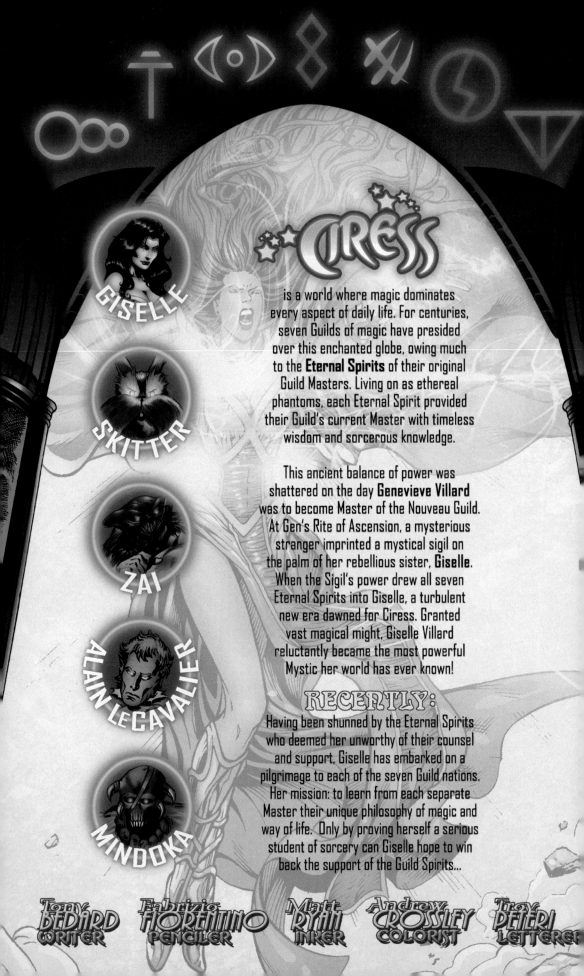

CIRESS

is a world where magic dominates every aspect of daily life. For centuries, seven Guilds of magic have presided over this enchanted globe, owing much to the **Eternal Spirits** of their original Guild Masters. Living on as ethereal phantoms, each Eternal Spirit provided their Guild's current Master with timeless wisdom and sorcerous knowledge.

This ancient balance of power was shattered on the day **Genevieve Villard** was to become Master of the Nouveau Guild. At Gen's Rite of Ascension, a mysterious stranger imprinted a mystical sigil on the palm of her rebellious sister, **Giselle**. When the Sigil's power drew all seven Eternal Spirits into Giselle, a turbulent new era dawned for Ciress. Granted vast magical might, Giselle Villard reluctantly became the most powerful Mystic her world has ever known!

RECENTLY:

Having been shunned by the Eternal Spirits who deemed her unworthy of their counsel and support, Giselle has embarked on a pilgrimage to each of the seven Guild nations. Her mission: to learn from each separate Master their unique philosophy of magic and way of life. Only by proving herself a serious student of sorcery can Giselle hope to win back the support of the Guild Spirits...

GISELLE

SKITTER

ZAI

ALAIN LeCAVALIER

MINDOKA

Tony **BEDARD** WRITER

Fabrizio **FIORENTINO** PENCILER

Matt **RYAN** INKER

Andrew **CROSSLEY** COLORIST

Troy **PETERI** LETTERER

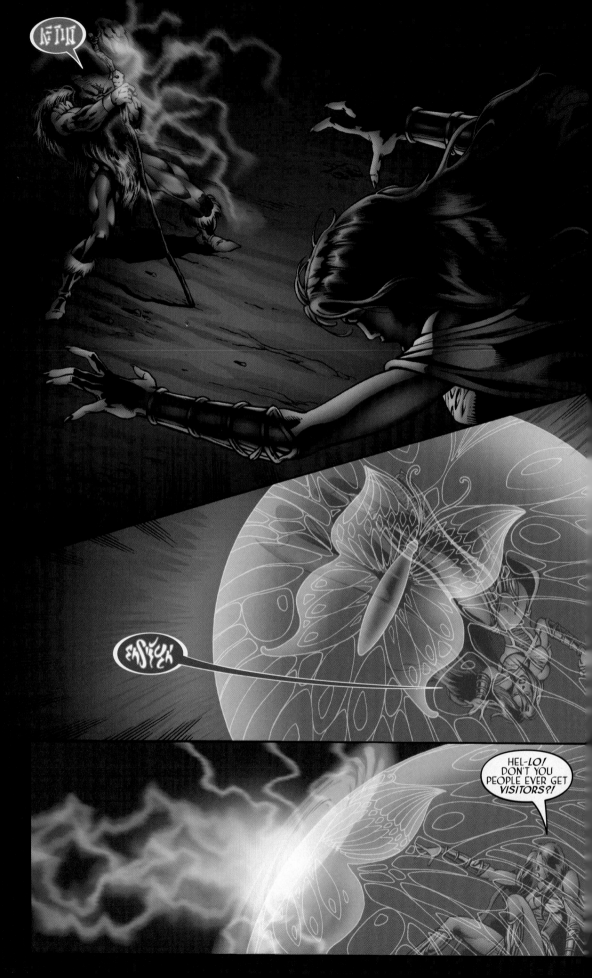

THERE HE IS.

GREETINGS, LeCAVALIER.

WE'VE MISSED YOUR COMPANY, ALAIN!

OH.

STILL FIXATED ON THAT HOPELESS GIRL? HOW DREARY.

COME, MINDOKA. THE NOUVEAU SPIRIT WILL REJOIN OUR FELLOWSHIP WHEN HE TIRES OF SEEING THAT GIRL DISGRACE HIS GUILD.

MINDOKA...?

HE'LL BE ALONG IN A MINUTE, HEROTUS.

PREPARE THE VILLAGE SQUARE FOR THE *WAKULUWE!*

LET EVERY MAN, WOMAN AND CHILD IN THE *KRAAL* TAKE PART!

WE WILL SHOW HER THE STEPS TO THE DANCE, BUT GISELLE WILL BE THE TRUE SHAMAN TODAY.

I BEG YOUR *PARDON?* I'M NO SHAMAN! YOU HAVEN'T TAUGHT ME A SINGLE *SPELL,* MUCH LESS THE *WACKY-LULU* DANCE!

I SAID EARLIER THAT I HAD NOTHING TO TEACH YOU BECAUSE YOU *ALREADY* CARRY ALL THE ANSWERS WITHIN YOU. *EVERYONE* DOES.

JUST AS EVERYBODY MUST FIND THEIR *OWN* PATH TO THE CENTRAL MOUNTAIN.

WE BELIEVE THAT EACH INDIVIDUAL MUST BE THE SHAMAN OF HIS *OWN* LIFE.

"KEEP IN MIND WHAT A SHAMAN *IS*. A SHAMAN IS SOMEONE WHO HAS A *DIRECT* EXPERIENCE OF THE MYSTICAL REALM.

"NOUVEAU PRIESTS, ENCHANTRESS NUNS, TANTRIC ACOLYTES, DARK MAGI MONKS... THESE ARE ALL MERE *FUNCTIONARIES* OF THEIR BELIEF SYSTEMS...

"...THEY *DESCRIBE* MYSTIC TRUTHS THAT SLUMBER BENEATH THE WAKING WORLD, AND THEY *SHOW* YOU WAYS OF LIVING IN ACCORD WITH THE SUPERNATURAL...

"BUT THE SHAMAN IS NOT TOLD, NOR SHOWN THE WAY. THE SHAMAN HEARS THE CALL, AND GOES TO *SEE* THESE THINGS *FOR HIMSELF.*

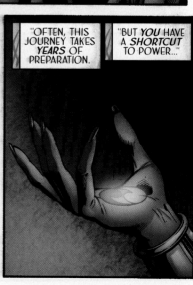

"OFTEN, THIS JOURNEY TAKES *YEARS* OF PREPARATION.

"BUT *YOU* HAVE A *SHORTCUT* TO POWER..."

"THE *WAKULUWE* CEREMONY IS MEDITATION IN MOTION.

"THE MOVEMENT AND RHYTHM STOP THE CHATTER IN YOUR HEAD, AND LET YOUR HEART LEAD THE WAY.

"SOMEWHERE JUST PAST ENDURANCE AND BEYOND YOUR COMPREHENSION, A DOOR OPENS TO THE NEXT WORLD...

"...YOU WILL *KNOW* IT WHEN YOU *SEE* IT."

MASTER ZAI...!

OMENS AND PORTENTS

❧ OUR PLAYERS ❧

SIMON ARCHARD
THE CITY'S FAVORITE SON, HIS MIND IS RAZOR-SHARP

EMMA BISHOP
A FETCHING BEAUTY, HER SPIRIT CRAVES ADVENTURE

MALCOLM LIGHTBOURNE
A CUNNING CRIMESMITH DESIGNS A DISASTROUS REVENGE

GARGOYLES BEHAVE CURIOUSLY

The citizenry of Partington have noted in recent days that the city's winged gargoyle populace has exhibited strange behaviour giving rise to fear of a rabid infestation of the commonly harmless creatures.

Self-described grottescologist Fenton Crombie offered that the otherwise benign gargoyles, now prone to gnashing their teeth at passing Partingtonians, are likely driven to some minor hysteria by the mysterious temblors jarring our city most fair since yesterday. Crombie likens the beasts to bellwethers on the order of canaries signaling deprivation of fresh air in gas-prone coalmines. But whereas these feathered birds silently succumb to suffocation, our own gargoyles may well be warning of dire events to yet transpire by their advancing excitable state •••**PLEASE CONTINUE INSIDE**

GARGOYLE EXPERT FENTON CROMBIE

WATER WEARY
CITY PLANNER FEARS DROUGHT

Selectmen met last evening in sequestered session to discuss what one city planner described on condition of anonymity as a precipitous concern to our potable drinking and bathing needs. In recent days, wells and cisterns throughout the city proper have risen and fallen to such degrees as to warrant alarm that reservoirs might run utterly dry. The aforementioned anonymous planner also offered forth that Partington's water resources might somehow be diverted at their source, perhaps due to subterranean shifts which•••**PLEASE CONTINUE INSIDE**

DETECTIVE MISSING

The *Arcadian* continues to await word from master detective Simon Archard to provide his account of solving the patricide of Mr. Wickston Oxford-Collins,

poisoned by his daughters and sole heirs to a millionaire's fortune. Archard and his erstwhile assistant Emma Bishop were last reported in pursuit of Malcolm Lightbourne, former partner of Archard and presumed accomplice to the Oxford-Collins murder •••**PLEASE CONTINUE INSIDE**

As It May Please the Court and Barristers of Our Fine Land:

 Scott **BEATTY** WRITER

 Paul **RYAN** Guest PENCILER

 Michael **PERKINS** INKER

 Val **STAPLES** Guest COLORIST

 Dave **LANPHEAR** LETTERER

YOUR *UNORTHODOX* STUDY HABITS, NO DOUBT.

...OR PERHAPS YOU'VE BEEN *DABBLING* IN *BLACK RITES?*

OH, NO...*NO*, MR. LIGHTBOURNE.

IT'S MERELY A *SCIENTIFIC* EXPLORATION.

I'VE POSTULATED THAT ONE CAN *FIX* THE TIME OF DEATH...

...BY EXAMINATION OF THE CONTENTS PRESENT IN THE DECEDENT'S GASTRIC PATH.

I *DID* AID THE POLICE IN A MURDER MYSTERY VERY RECENTLY.

DO TELL.

IT WAS *NOTHING*, REALLY...A KILLING UNSOLVED FOR FAR TOO LONG.

I HELPED THE INVESTIGATORS IDENTIFY THE CULPRIT BY MATCHING THE PRINTS OF HIS FINGERS TO IMPRESSIONS ON THE POOR BOY'S WRUNG NECK.

I CALL IT *FINGER-TYPING*.

A USEFUL BIT OF INFORMATION...

...PERHAPS AS IMPORTANT AS THE VICTIM'S OWN NAME.

MICHAEL LIGHTBOURNE.

QUITE SO.

YOU'VE DEMONSTRATED MORE FORWARD-THINKING IN YOUR *AMATEUR* INVESTIGATIONS THAN PARTINGTON'S FINEST HAVE SHOWN IN THRICE THAT TIME.

BUT, SIR... I'M NOT THE MOST *CONVERSATIONAL* SORT.

I'VE NEVER HAD MANY FRIENDS. NOT IN THE ORPHAN HOUSE, NOT HERE...

AND YOU'RE THE *BETTER* FOR IT.

TRUST ME, SIMON...

302

ARCHARD

BARTLESB

SOMERS, R.

O'HERLIHY, D.

...FRIENDSHIP AND LOYALTY WILL BE NOTHING MORE THAN IMPEDIMENTS TO YOUR *GREATER* CALLING...

THANKFULLY, A DRAMATIC *PAUSE.* HAVING SURVIVED MALCOLM LIGHTBOURNE'S WATERWORKS ENGINEERED TO SWALLOW UP PARTINGTON, SIMON AND I FIND OURSELVES SUBJECTED TO A VERY *DIFFERENT* TORTURE.

LIGHTBOURNE IS TRAPPED AMONG THE SODDEN WRECKAGE, YET WIELDS A DRY AND DEADLY FIREARM...AND AWFUL TRUTHS LONG *UNREVEALED.*

DID YOU *REALLY* MEET HIM THIS WAY, SIMON?

OF COURSE HE *DID,* MISS BISHOP!

IT WAS LIKELY THE BEST DAY OF *BOTH* OUR LIVES, EH, SIMON?

"IN JUST FIVE YEARS, OUR RENOWN HAD GROWN CONSIDERABLY... AS HAD OUR *CLIENTELE.*"

"THE EPIPHANIC CHURCH RARELY EMPLOYED OUTSIDERS IN THEIR AFFAIRS.

"OUR INVOLVEMENT WAS *TESTAMENT* TO THE FAR-REACHING REPUTATION OF LIGHTBOURNE AND ARCHARD..."

...WHOSE INVESTIGATORY SKILLS ARE *UNSURPASSED,* I HEAR TELL.

PERHAPS THEN YOU MIGHT SEE FIT TO TRAIN YOUR DEDUCTIVE *LIGHT* UPON A CASE OF STOLEN PROPERTY.

AN ARTIFACT ONLY RECENTLY UNEARTHED AND OF GREAT...*CONCERN*... TO THE CHURCH HAS GONE MISSING, ABSCONDED FROM OUR CARE.

THERE WAS NO BETTER PUPIL...

SO EAGER TO *LEARN*, SO EAGER TO *PLEASE* HIS *MENTOR*...

HE...HE... ehn...MY LEG IS *SHATTERED*... RENT IN TWO.

I CAN SEE *BONE*... AND I SEEM TO BE LOSING QUITE A LOT OF BLOOD.

IF NOT FOR *SHOCK*, I VENTURE I WOULD NOT BE SO LUCID ABOUT...ihn... *THE PAST.*

SHALL I... ihn...SHALL I *CONTINUE?*

YOUR *WORSHIP*, PERHAPS IF YOU COULD BE MORE *SPECIFIC* ABOUT THIS ITEM --

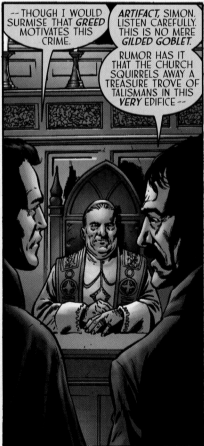

-- THOUGH I WOULD SURMISE THAT *GREED* MOTIVATES THIS CRIME.

ARTIFACT, SIMON. LISTEN CAREFULLY. THIS IS NO MERE *GILDED GOBLET.*

RUMOR HAS IT THAT THE CHURCH SQUIRRELS AWAY A TREASURE TROVE OF TALISMANS IN THIS *VERY* EDIFICE --

-- *SORCEROUS* ARTIFACTS KEPT UNDER LOCK AND LATCH TO GUARD US LESS *ENLIGHTENED* FROM THEIR SINISTER INFLUENCE.

AM I NOT *CORRECT*, YOUR *WORSHIP?*

MAGIC IS NOTHING BUT *POPPYCOCK.*

IF ONLY THAT WERE *TRUE*, MR. ARCHARD...

BUT THIS POPPYCOCK HAS A *NAME*.

ACCORDING TO SCRIPTURE IT IS A JEWEL OF NEFARIOUS POWER.

AND IN OUR TONGUE IT IS KNOWN IN CERTAIN INFAMY AS THE *ENIGMATIC PRISM*.

SOME SORT OF *SORCEROR'S STONE*? SURELY YOU ARE *JESTING*, FATHER...

THE *ENIGMATIC PRISM*...

"CLEARLY YOU ARE *INFORMED* ON PENBERTHY'S TRAVELS, MR. LIGHTBOURNE.

"THE CHURCH, EXPECTING HIS ARRIVAL, DISPATCHED TWO EMISSARIES THIS MORN TO ACCOMPANY THE PRISM TO MY CHARGE.

"THEY WERE LATER FOUND DEAD, PENBERTHY HIMSELF GONE *MISSING*.

"THE JEWEL'S *CURSE* HAS LIKELY STRUCK ONCE MORE.

"NO ONE KNOWS ITS ORIGINS, THOUGH THE PRISM IS BELIEVED TO BE MANY CENTURIES OLD...ITS VALUE *INCALCULABLE*.

"AS SUCH, IT HAS RARELY PASSED HANDS THROUGH *BENIGN* CIRCUMSTANCE.

"THERE ARE WHISPERS THAT THE JEWEL IS *ALLURING*...

"TO GAZE INTO ITS RADIANT FIRE IS TO LOSE SIGHT OF *ALL* REASON AND DESIRE NOTHING BUT THE *PRISM ITSELF*...

"...TO SURRENDER TO ONE'S *BASEST* DESIRES."

I HAD THOUGHT IT ONLY *LEGEND.*

SIMON, IF IT INDEED *EXISTS*--

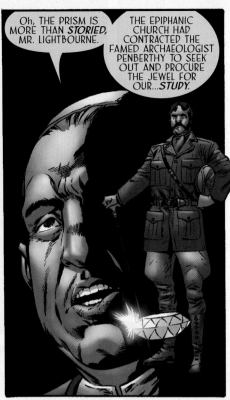

Oh, THE PRISM IS MORE THAN *STORIED,* MR. LIGHTBOURNE.

THE EPIPHANIC CHURCH HAD CONTRACTED THE FAMED ARCHAEOLOGIST PENBERTHY TO SEEK OUT AND PROCURE THE JEWEL FOR OUR...*STUDY.*

CLIVE PENBERTHY, THE ADVENTURER WHOSE SHIP WAS INBOUND FOR PARTINGTON THIS VERY MORNING?

A TRICK OF E LIGHT, YOUR EMINENCE.

LIGHT REFRACTED IN SUCH A WAY TO RESEMBLE FLAMES.

AND IN OUR XPERIENCE, AVARICE *LWAYS* BRINGS OUT THE WORST IN MAN--

SIMON, MIGHT I *REMIND* YOU THAT A PRISM, BY DEFINITION, IS A MEDIUM WHICH *MISREPRESENTS* THE VIEW SPIED THROUGH IT.

THE *ENIGMATIC PRISM* MAY WELL DISTORT ITS HOLDER'S VIEW OF THE WORLD, AND BY EXTENSION... THE HOLDER *HIMSELF.*

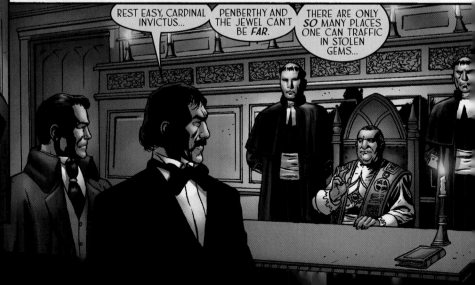

REST EASY, CARDINAL INVICTUS...

PENBERTHY AND THE JEWEL CAN'T BE *FAR.*

THERE ARE ONLY *SO* MANY PLACES ONE CAN TRAFFIC IN STOLEN GEMS...

"...EVEN ONES WITH *MAGICAL* PROPERTIES."

COVER THE DOOR, SIMON.

LET US COMMENCE OUR INTERROGATIONS IN *PRIVATE*.

COME THEN, COLQUIN...

CLIVE PENBERT

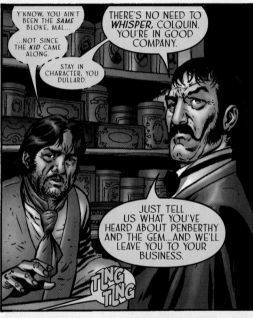

Y'KNOW, YOU AIN'T BEEN THE *SAME* BLOKE, MAL...

...NOT SINCE THE *KID* CAME ALONG.

STAY IN CHARACTER, YOU DULLARD.

THERE'S NO NEED TO *WHISPER*, COLQUIN. YOU'RE IN GOOD COMPANY.

JUST TELL US WHAT YOU'VE HEARD ABOUT PENBERTHY AND THE GEM...AND WE'LL LEAVE YOU TO YOUR BUSINESS.

TING TING

MIND WHAT YER *SNITCHIN'*, COLQUIN.

THERE'S MORE'N US LOOKIN' FOR MISTER PENBERTHY AND THAT BAD LUCK OF A *ROCK*.

--THEN YOU MIGHT JUST NEED SOME SENSE *KNOCKED* INTO THAT HIGHBROW HEAD OF YOUR'N...

KRKK

KKLUNK

KLOD

SNEAKY BLIGHTER...

SURELY, PARTINGTON'S MOST *LOQUACIOUS* INFORMANT MUST HAVE *SOMETHING* TO SAY ON THIS MATTER?

MORE MONEY TO PASS ALONG TO PENNY? CREDITORS BARKIN' DOWN HIS DOOR?

JUST PLAY ALONG AND FEIGN A BIT OF FRIGHT...

Uh... RIGHT.

...*DON'T HIT ME!*

STRIKE YOU, COLQUIN? *WHATEVER* GAVE YOU SUCH A THOUGHT?

WELL, THE WAY YOU'RE LEVELING THAT WALKING STICK LIKE IT'S A PIKE FOR A PIG...

MERELY EMBELLISHING MY *POINT*, COLQUIN.

CONTINUE.

...THERE'S... uh...THERE'S *LOTS* OF SCUTTLEBUTT CIRCULATING ABOUT ON PENNY...uh... *PENBERTHY.*

GO ON.

I'D EVEN WAGER T'SAY THAT ME AN' ROLLY ARE WILLIN' T'GO *FARTHER* FOR BOTH OF 'EM.

RIGHT, ROLLY?

RIGHT, NASH.

SO, IF YOU THINK THAT PONCY *CANE* IS A MATCH FOR ROLLY'S BLADE OR MY *SAP--*

K KLOP

YOU WERE *SAYING,* MISTER NASH?

BRAVO, SIMON. WE WERE LIKELY OUTMATCHED IN BRAWN, YET YOU MEASURED THE SITUATION AND APTLY USED THE FIELD OF BATTLE TO OUR *ADVANTAGE.*

I THOUGHT IT BEST TO HASTEN OUR EXIT AND CONTINUE THE HUNT. WHERE NOW?

PERHAPS WE SHOULD COMMENCE TO WHERE *ALL* OF MISTER PENBERTHY'S TREASURES GO...

"PARTINGTON'S ARCHIVE OF ANTIQUITIES.

"WHERE ELSE WOULD ONE EXPECT TO FIND A TREASURE-HUNTER AND HIS ILL-GOTTEN BOOTY?"

YOUR HELP IS MUCH *APPRECIATED*, DOCTOR SMITHEE.

OF ALL THE ITEMS I CURATE, THIS I'M AFRAID IS *ALL* WE HAVE IN THE COLLECTION WHICH MAKES MENTION OF THE ENIGMATIC PRISM.

SKASH

...AND I WILL PROCEED TO *DE-CLAW* MISTER PENBERTHY.

NOT BLOODY LIKELY!

THE CLAWS OF SEPTA ARE *KEEN* BLADES...

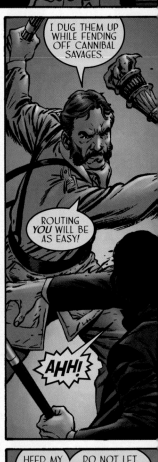

I DUG THEM UP WHILE FENDING OFF CANNIBAL SAVAGES.

ROUTING *YOU* WILL BE AS EASY!

AHH!

HEED MY WORDS, SIMON.

DO NOT LET IT HAPPEN *EVER* AGAIN.

PENBERTHY WON'T GET FAR.

THE SECOND LEVEL...!

A PRECISION EAR AS ALWAYS, SIMON...

I *FOUND* YOU AND I'LL *KEEP* YOU...

CLAWS OF SEPTA
COURTESY OF
PENBERTHY EXPEDITION

MISTER PENBERTHY, I PRESUME?

WHAT DO YOU WANT WITH ME?!

BAR THE DOOR, SIMON...

KRASH

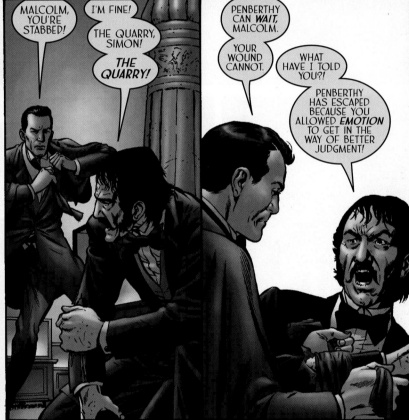

MALCOLM, YOU'RE STABBED!

I'M FINE! THE QUARRY, SIMON! *THE QUARRY!*

PENBERTHY CAN *WAIT*, MALCOLM.

YOUR WOUND CANNOT.

WHAT HAVE I TOLD YOU?!

PENBERTHY HAS ESCAPED BECAUSE YOU ALLOWED *EMOTION* TO GET IN THE WAY OF BETTER JUDGMENT!

I SUSPECT I KNOW WHERE HE'LL APPEAR NEXT.

AND I BELIEVE CARDINAL INVICTUS CAN CONFIRM MY THOUGHTS IF HE WILL ANSWER JUST *ONE* QUESTION.

WELL, *THAT* CERTAINLY EXPLAINS A GREAT DEAL.

DON'T JUDGE HIM TOO *HARSHLY,* MISS BISHOP.

SIMON ARCHARD MAY BE A COLD FISH BY MY OWN *ENCOURAGEMENT...*

BUT FOR WHAT HE LACKS IN *EMPATHY,* SIMON MAKES UP IN INTELLIGENCE AND REASONING SKILL BEYOND THE AVERAGE.

HE'S A *SMART* ONE, OUR BOY... ALBEIT AMBIVALENT TO A FAULT.

HE DOES ME *PROUD.*

"I ASSURE YOU THAT *THIS* WAS NOT THE CASE ALL THOSE YEARS AGO, ESPECIALLY AFTER HE HAD DEFEATED HIS STAMMER.

"INTERESTINGLY, AS WE HURRIED AFTER PENBERTHY... SIMON POINTED OUT THE IRONY THAT OUR QUEST FOR THE ENIGMATIC PRISM WOULD BOTH *BEGIN* AND *END* AT THE EPIPHANIC CHURCH.

"ACTUALLY, THAT'S NOT QUITE TRUE.

"IT WOULD END IN THE CHURCH'S INFAMOUS *MUSEUM OBSCURA.*

SIMON, CAN ALL THIS BE *TRUE?*

I HAD ASSUMED THAT YOU WERE BIRTHED...FULLY... FORMED...

YOU... YOU'RE NOT *LISTENING.*

*A*ND WHY *SHOULD* HE?

ALTHOUGH LIGHTBOURNE IS AMUSED BY THIS PROMENADE DOWN MEMORY LANE, SIMON DOESN'T SHARE HIS MERRIMENT.

NONE OF THIS IS LAUGHABLE TO SIMON...AND THE REASONS NO DOUBT ARE ABOUT TO BE FULLY ILLUMINATED.

QUITE UNCHARACTERISTIC OF HIM TO BE SO *LACONIC*, MISS BISHOP.

KRITCH KRITCH

"PENBERTHY HAD BEEN THERE *BEFORE,* OF COURSE. HIS EMINENCE *CONFIRMED* THAT TO SIMON'S INQUIRY.

"PENBERTHY'S BALLYHOOED EXPEDITIONS HAD, IN FACT, *STOCKED* THIS SECRET CACHE OF ARCANE ARTIFACTS.

"HE KNEW THIS PLACE ALL TOO WELL.

"IMAGINE HIS SURPRISE THEN WHEN HE EYED THE ENIGMATIC PRISM HIDING *IN PLAIN SIGHT.*"

BUT... BUT...

...HOW CAN THE GEM BE *THERE* WHEN I'VE GOT IT TUCKED SAFELY AWAY RIGHT--

--HERE?

"PENBERTHY THEN DECIDED THAT *TWO* ENIGMATIC PRISMS WERE FAR MORE BEAUTIFUL THAN JUST THE ONE."

FALS

MY EYES!

PERHAPS THE DIAMOND DAGGER WILL *FINISH* YOU OFF RIGHT.

STAY OUT OF THIS, SIMON.

MISTER PENBERTHY AND I HAVE *UNFINISHED* BUSINESS.

TIME TO PAY FOR YOUR CRIMES, *CLIVE.*

MY CRIMES?!

TIME FOR *EACH* OF US TO PAY, I SUSPECT... *MALCOLM.*

YOU'LL NEVER KNOW!

NONE OF THESE TRINKETS CAN COMPARE!

CLIVE, THE *LAMP!*

WHAT OF IT?

THE PRISM HAS SURVIVED DISASTER BEFORE--

THOK

NO!

CAN'T... SEE...

A DECOY-- --A FALSE GEM FILLED WITH FLASH POWDER TO HELP YOU SEE THE *LIGHT*, PENBERTHY...YOU ARE WITHIN THE *EPIPHANIC* CHURCH, AFTER ALL.

BUT THE PRISM *BLINDS* A MAN TO REASON, DOES IT NOT?

OR WAS THE GEM'S THEFT MERELY A *DIVERSION*? A RUSE TO DIVERT INTEREST FROM YOUR PLUNDER OF THE MUSEUM OBSCURA?

PITY THE CLAWS OF SEPTA DIDN'T CUT YOU *DEEPER*, DETECTIVE.

DIAMOND DAGGER OF KHAN SINGH

THE PRISM IS INDEED A BEAUTIFUL BAUBLE, CLIVE.

SO TEMPTING...SO *IRRESISTIBLE*.

IS IT REALLY *WORTH* ALL THE EFFORT?

KKKTKSS

IT'S MINE!

YOU SAID IT YOURSELF, MISTER PENBERTHY...

I FOUND IT, *I* SHALL *KEEP* IT.

BUT I KILLED FOR IT!

I... I...

SKUCH

YOU DON'T *DESERVE* IT, CLIVE.

YOU KILLED HIM.

LEST HE KILL *YOU*, SIMON. I SAVED YOUR UNGRATEFUL LIFE AND I DID IT WITH AN EMOTIONAL DETACHMENT YOU HAVE *YET* TO LEARN.

I KNOW NOW THAT THE LEGENDS ARE *FALSE*. THE PRISM DOES NOT DISTORT ONE'S WORLDVIEW... IT *CLARIFIES* IT. I *ALONE* SHOULD POSSESS IT.

CAN YOU SEE THE FLICKER OF BLUE FIRE AT ITS CENTER?

A TRICK OF THE LIGHT, SIMON?

DOES IT DANCE FOR YOU ALSO?

SIMON, THE *FIRE*. WE HAVEN'T MUCH TIME. LET'S DISCUSS THIS LATER LIKE OLD *FRIENDS*.

NO, MALCOLM. WE DISCUSS IT *NOW*.

I IMAGINE YOU CONVINCED PENBERTHY THAT *YOU* COULD EASE HIS MONEY WOES BY ENGINEERING A CRIME THAT PARTINGTON'S GREATEST DETECTIVE *COULDN'T* SOLVE.

DO YOU WISH ME TO ADMIT IT ALL?

IS THAT THE AFFIRMATION YOU DESIRE?

WOULD THAT MAKE YOU FEEL BETTER... *SMARTER*...THAN ME, SIMON?

VERY WELL, THEN...*HAVE* YOUR CONFESSION --

I DID IT.

I TOLD PENBERTHY THAT HE'D BEEN BETRAYED, HIMSELF *ROBBED* OF A LIFETIME OF SERVICE.

PLEASE GIVE IT TO ME BEFORE I DO SOMETHING *RASH.*

I'M VERY SORRY, MALCOLM.

I CANNOT.

CAN NOT OR *WILL* NOT?

THIS IS *OPPORTUNITY,* SIMON...PENBERTHY WILL SUFFER ALL THE BLAME AND THE PRISM CAN BE *OURS.*

SWALLOW YOUR TREPIDATION. CLIVE PENBERTHY HAD TO DIE... *DESERVED* TO DIE...

...SURELY YOU CAN *SEE* THAT INEVITABILITY.

ALL I SEE ARE *YOUR* HANDS CAREFULLY MANIPULATING THIS TERRIBLE AFFAIR.

I *OVERHEARD* YOUR LITTLE MORALITY PLAY AT THE TOBACCONIST...MY *"PRECISION EAR"* AND ALL.

PENBERTHY MUST HAVE BEEN IN *DIRE* FINANCIAL STRAITS...UTTERLY *DESPERATE...*

...AND YOU *KNEW,* DIDN'T YOU?

BUT THE GREEDY SOT WANTED MORE THAN HIS DUSTY *JUNK,* RUNNING OFF WHILE I DISPATCHED THOSE EPIPHANIC ERRAND BOYS ON THE DOCK.

AND... AND...

AND I WOULD HAVE GOTTEN AWAY WITH IT IF NOT FOR MY DAMNABLE *ASSISTANT!*

YOUR *PARTNER,* YOU MEAN!

DELAY NO FURTHER, SIMON. YOU KNOW FULL WELL *WHO'S* IN CHARGE!

NOW GIVE ME THE PRISM!

THAT'S THE *DEEPEST* CUT OF ALL... ISN'T IT, SIMON?

THAT I AM LESS THAN YOU... *HUMAN.*

OR DOES YOUR PAIN COME FROM KNOWING THAT I HAD FOOLED YOU SO *EASILY?*

MALCOLM...

-- FRIEND?

NO. LEAVE ME.

WHAT ARE YOU SAYING?

JUST GO.

CONSIDER THE BUSINESS *YOURS.*

YOU ARE INDEED THE *MASTER SLEUTH,* SIMON.

PLEASE TAKE MY HAND, MALCOLM...

...I CAN'T LEAVE YOU TO DIE.

SIMON, YOU TRULY ARE *WITLESS...*

ALL THESE YEARS GONE, YOU ARE STILL SO EASILY MANEUVERED.

LEAVE *YOU* THE AGENCY? *FAH!* YOU'RE NOT FIT TO WALK IN MY SHADOW.

IT'S HIGH TIME I TOOK LEAVE OF *YOU.* IN FACT, WHY NOT CONSIDER YOUR UNIMPRESSIVE EMPLOYMENT --

-- TERMINATED.

MAL--?

SHUK

WHEN ALL IS SAID AND DONE, YOUR *NOTORIETY* WILL BE AS PENBERTHY'S FELLOW *CONSPIRATOR.*

AND THE PRISM WILL BE ASSUMED *LOST* IN YOUR GRASP AMID THE CONFLAGRATION.

OF COURSE, I WILL HAVE PLUCKED THE GEM FROM YOUR RIGOR-STIFF HAND *BEFORE* THE--

OH, NO...

NO!

NOOOO

"I SUPPOSE I HAD THAT COMING."

DON'T LOOK SO *SURPRISED,* SIMON.

YOUR DEMISE WAS INEVITABLE.

ALL THESE YEARS WERE BETTER SPENT GROOMING A *PATSY* THAN A PARTNER.

I HAD THAT *EPIPHANY* QUITE SOME TIME AGO.

BACK WHEN THE THOUGHT OF POSSESSING THE ENIGMATIC PRISM HELD JUST A *GLIMMER* OF HOPE.

THE FALL DIDN'T KILL ME...AND NEITHER DID TREADING THE WAVES BENEATH THE EPIPHANIC CATHEDRAL.

I WON'T BORE YOU WITH THE INCONSEQUENTIALS.

YOU'VE ALREADY GUESSED THAT I CONVALESCED AMONG GYPSIES WHILE ALL ASSUMED I WAS QUITE--

--*DEAD.*

SIMON, HOW DID YOU...

YES, SIMON...HOW *DID* YOU SURVIVE YOUR SKEWERING, NOT TO MENTION THE BURNING MUSEUM?

OBVIOUSLY, MY SCARS SHOW FULL WELL THAT THE FLAMES TOUCHED *ME* EVEN AS I FELL.

I DON'T KNOW, MALCOLM.

PERHAPS I EXPERIENCED MY *OWN* EPIPHANY.

I REMEMBER A BOLT OF LIGHT... AND THEN I AWOKE IN A SANATORIUM WITH NO OTHER MEMORY OF MY ESCAPE.

I THOUGHT YOU *ROSE* FROM THE GRAVE TO KILL ME, MALCOLM...

BUT YOU ONLY CAME BACK FOR THE PRISM.

ACTUALLY...

I CAME BACK FOR *BOTH*.

AND IF I CAN'T HAVE *ONE*...

...I'LL HAVE THE OTHER!

BLAM BLAM

DOWN, EMMA!

NO, SIMON... NOT--

--buh... *THE WATER.*

LIGHTBOURNE?

GONE. HE FIRED HIS TWO SHOTS.

GIVEN THE STATE OF HIS SUBTERRANEAN LAIR, HE'S LIKELY GONE *ABOVE* GROUND NOW.

WE NEED TO FIND HIS BOLTHOLE TO THE SURFACE.

IMMEDIATELY.

YES, OF COURSE... JUST ALLOW ME A MOMENT TO CATCH MY BREATH.

WE HAVEN'T THE TIME, EMMA.

WE'VE GOT TO FIND MALCOLM *NOW*--

--BEFORE HE REALIZES HE ALREADY *HAS* THE ENIGMATIC PRISM!

*H*AD WE TRULY SEEN THE LIGHT, BOTH SIMON AND I WOULD HAVE REALIZED THAT SURVIVING LIGHTBOURNE ONCE WAS *HAPPENSTANCE.*

TWICE COULD LIKELY BE MERE *COINCIDENCE.*

A THIRD TIME WOULD SURELY CALL FOR NO LESS THAN DIVINE *PROVIDENCE.*

THE FIRST

IN THE BEGINNING...

They were the gods who created the universe before descending into a constant state of war. Then their home, Elysia, was torn by the Eidolon rift as Altwaal separated the First into two Houses to end the warfare. Peace and boredom followed. Now the First have been catalyzed into action with the appearance of the Sigil-Bearers, beings of great power that was *not* given to them by the First, one of whom killed one of the First. If these Sigil-Bearers can destroy the First...their godhood itself is in question.

HOUSE SINISTER

HOUSE DEXTER

INGRA
the SEETHING BEAUTY

ORIUM
the ORACLE

GANNISH
the SUFFERER

PERSHA
the UNIFIER

Gannish the truthseeker returns from Earth to find that **Ingra**, Leader of House Sinister, has been overthrown by a small group of conspirators: **Seahn**, a recent convert to Sinister's side; Braag, whom Ingra thought was her toy; **Orium**, the mad seer and former Leader who may be saner than he appears; and Enson, Seahn's enigmatic friend and protector. Challenging the conspirators, Gannish receives from Enson a vision that compels him along a new path. **Persha**, **Pyrem's** daughter, tries to get Pyrem to go to the rescue of Ingra, her mother. **Trenin** prepares to hunt down Seahn much as he pursued his mother Tulity, would-be assassin of the Leader of all First, Altwaal, centuries ago. Tulity birthed and abandoned her baby to escape Trenin, who patiently waited with the child for her return. When she did not, he chose a different tactic, deceit, the same tactic he uses now. Trenin travels to House Sinister, sneaking inside with his power intact and his face changed...

PYREM
the DIPLOMAT

TRENIN
the HUNTER

YALA
the WARRIOR WOMAN

SEAHN
the DISSIDENT

CHAPTER 21
Barbara **KESEL** WRITER
Andy **SMITH** PENCILER
Brad **VANCATA** INKER
Jung **CHOI** COLORIST
Dave **LANPHEAR** LETTERER

CHAPTER 22
Barbara **KESEL** WRITER
Andrea **DI VITO** PENCILER
Rob **HUNTER** INKER
Rob **SCHWAGER** COLORIST
Dave **LANPHEAR** LETTERER

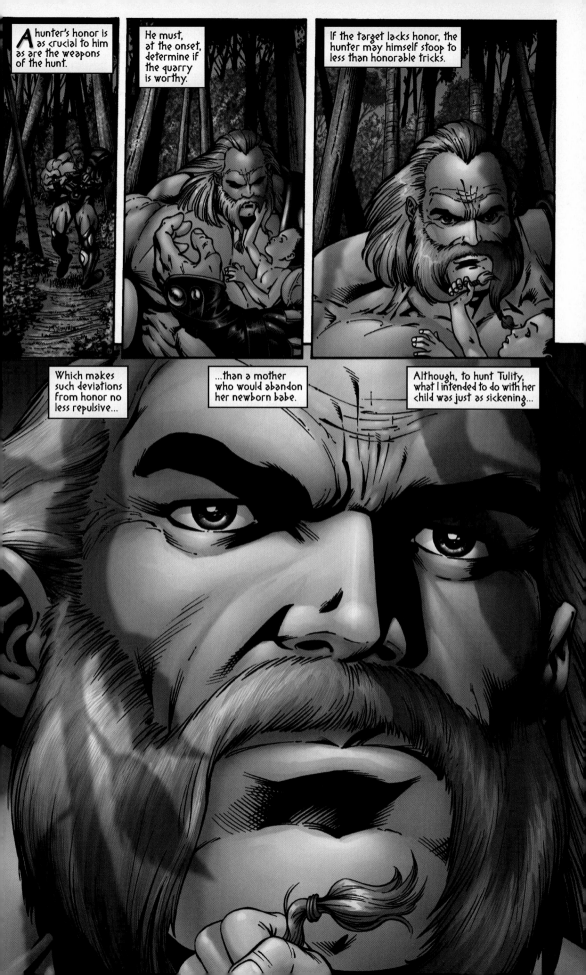

A hunter's honor is as crucial to him as are the weapons of the hunt.

He must, at the onset, determine if the quarry is worthy.

If the target lacks honor, the hunter may himself stoop to less than honorable tricks.

Which makes such deviations from honor no less repulsive...

...than a mother who would abandon her newborn babe.

Although, to hunt Tulity, what I intended to do with her child was just as sickening...

Better the child be thought my half-blood spawn...

...than my tool towards his mother's execution.

It was only a matter of time...

...which drifted past.

When the hunter is too long on the trail--

--the mind plays tricks--

--sees what isn't there--

TULITY!

KEEP YOUR HANDS FROM THE CHILD, TULITY!

KEEP YOUR *OWN* CLEAR, TRENIN-- HE'S *MY* CHILD, NOT YOURS!

MINE TO DO WITH--

misses what is.

AHHH...

...COME TO ME, MY BABY BOY!

KRNGK

NOOO!

HI.

--AS I PLEASE!

WHAPPT

SEAHN!

YOU'VE NAMED HIM?

THAT WAS MY RIGHT, TRENIN. SO HE'S YOURS...FOR NOW.

ARE YOU HARMED, LAD?

NAH.

BUT THESE CHAOTIC TIMES CALL FOR A DECISIVE LEADER.

HERE'S A DECISION--

WE NEED TO BE PREPARED FOR RESISTANCE FROM HOUSE DEXTER.

WE'LL CONSCRIPT THE SECUNDAE INTO MILITIAS.

PREPARING FOR WAR SHOULD KEEP THEM FROM ACTING UP THE WAY THE DEXTER SECUNDAE DID.

AT *MY* INSTIGATION! WITHOUT MY PRODDING, THEY WERE AS PASSIVE AS--WHA--?

ENSON--?

STAY WITH ME, HERE.

JUST LETTING AN OLD FRIEND PASS.

HMMM?

OLD FRIEND? BUT *WHO*--?

HE'S NO ONE YOU KNOW NOW.

YOU LOOK AS THOUGH YOU'VE SEEN YOUR OWN GHOST, SEAHN.

YOU KNOW ME? I DON'T KNOW YOU, DO I?

LET THE STRANGER *GO,* SEAHN.

HERE'S *ANOTHER* DECISION-- WE CARVE BACK THE MASS OF INGRA'S CASTLE TO OPEN A PLAZA, RIGHT *HERE.*

BOLD MOVE.

BOLD? NOW YOU'RE ON BRAAG'S SIDE?

ENSON, I--

UNNH!

THE BOLD MOVE WAS *MINE*--CLEARLY, *NOTHING* FOOLS ENSON.

TRENIN. YOU'RE *TRENIN*.

I'VE CLAIMED HUNT ON YOU, *SEAHN*.

YOU HAVE TWO *CHOICES*--

GIVE YOURSELF OVER TO ME TO FACE JUSTICE IN HOUSE DEXTER--

--OR *DIE*.

I *KNEW* YOU WOULDN'T LET IT REST!

NOT AFTER GRACO GOT KILLED.

LISTEN TO ME!

I'LL NEVER GO BACK, TRENIN! *THIS* IS MY HOME NOW!

THEN YOU CHOOSE TO DIE?

HUHH!

YOU'D *REALLY* KILL YOUR *SON?*

YOU--!

WHAT WILL IT TAKE FOR YOU TO SEE THAT YOU'RE NOT *MINE,* SEAHN?

FORGIVE MY INTERRUPTION, TRENIN...

I AM **SICK** OF --

EH?

...EVEN THOUGH I ADMIRE YOUR AUDACITY, I CANNOT LET YOU SUCCEED.

ENSON?

DAMN YOU, CREATURE!

YOU'RE **ALWAYS** INTERFERING!

YES, I **AM**!

AND I WILL AGAIN AND AGAIN, AND **AGAIN**!

FORGIVE ME--

--I PREFER--

--TO KEEP CONTROL.

CONTROL?

FEEL BETTER?

AS I SAID, I **WILL** INTERFERE...

...AS MANY TIMES AS IT TAKES TO GET YOU READY.

READY?

FOR **WHAT**?

"...THEY'RE A PATIENT BUNCH, BUT I'D PREFER NOT TO KEEP THE COUNCIL WAITING."

GREETINGS ORDIAL, INDORIENNE.

BE WARNED-- IT'S TRUE.

HE'S BRINGING INGRA'S CHILD.

TO COUNCIL?

A SINISTER SECUNDAE?

ARE WE TO WELCOME HER AS AN EQUAL?

GANI, YOU CAN BE SURE THAT HER *MOTHER'S* BEHIND THE GIRL'S APPEARANCE HERE.

INGRA'S NOT ABOVE USING HER OWN CHILD TO GET WHAT SHE WANTS.

SCHULLUN, PERSHA IS ALSO *PYREM'S* CHILD.

REMEMBER *HIS* STRENGTH OF WILL.

BETWEEN THEM, THEY'VE CREATED A PASSIONATE EMPATH.

A DANGEROUS COMBINATION.

AAAAHHH...

...listen TO YOUR FINE WHINES!

SAVE FOR TRENIN, THE COUNCIL IS COMPLETE.

GO INSIDE. TELL THEM YOUR STORY--

WELCOME, PYREM. AM I TO--?

ALLOW MY DAUGHTER THROUGH THE VEIL OF PRIVACY, IHROE?

YES.

DAUGHTER...

PYREM, DON'T LEAVE ME--

PLEAD YOUR CASE WITH *THEM*, PERSHA. I BACK WHATEVER DECISION THEY MAKE.

AND *I* HOPE THAT ALTWAAL'S FAITH IN ME WAS JUSTIFIED...

THE HIGH COUNCIL OF DEXTER WELCOMES YOU, PERSHA OF SINISTER.

PERHAPS YOU WILL EXPLAIN TO US WHY PYREM CALLED US ON YOUR BEHALF?

COUNCIL ELDERS, I KNOW YOU BY YOUR NAMES, BUT NOT ALL YOUR FACES.

PLEASE ALLOW ME TO TRY AND MATCH THE TWO--

YALA.

ANTEM.

REASH.

GANI.

SCHULLUN.

RAAMIA.

INDORIENNE.

ORDIAL.

BEING SECUNDAE, AND INGRA'S CHILD, I HAVEN'T BEEN ALLOWED TO MEET MANY OF YOU, BUT YOU ALL KNOW MY FATHER...

...*PYREM*...

...AND BEING *FIRST*, I'M CERTAIN YOU'VE ALL MET MY *MOTHER*.

I AM *NOT* HERE AS HER AGENT, NOR WOULD SHE WANT ME TO BE HERE.

I'M HERE TO PLEAD FOR YOUR HELP TO SAVE *ALL* OF THE FIRST.

SAVE US?

GO ON...

FROM?

BECAUSE I USED HIS *GAUNTLET* TO GUIDE ME TO HIS SIDE.

*H*IS GAUNTLET?

HOW DID *YOU* COME TO POSSESS IT..?

...AND WHERE HAS IT GONE?

IT'S...

...NOT HERE.

I LEFT IT...

...WITH A FRIEND...

...SOME- WHERE.

YOU HAD ONE OF THE MOST POWERFUL OF ALTWAAL'S WEAPONS AND YOU *DON'T KNOW* WHERE IT IS?

*I*NDORIENNE!

THE GIRL'S HOUSE SINISTER!

YOU CAN'T EXPECT HER TO TELL US *ALL* HER SECRETS...

...NOT RIGHT AWAY.

IF SHE *DID* SEE ALTWAAL...

...AND HE *DID* SAY WHAT SHE SAYS...

...THEN YOU KNOW *I'LL* BE INTERESTED IN HEARING *more.*

WHO **KNOWS** WHAT IT'S DONE TO HIS PSYCHOLOGICAL DEVELOPMENT!

YOU'VE BROUGHT ME **MANY** STRAYS OVER THE CENTURIES, BUT YOU'VE **NEVER** STAYED TO WATCH THEM, AND YOU'VE NEVER DONE **ANYTHING** THIS CRUEL.

WHAT MAKES THIS ONE DIFFERENT?

WHY ARE YOU DOING THIS TO HIM, LOVE?

I NEED HIM YOUNG AND VULNERABLE.

THIS BOY IS CAUGHT IN A HORRIBLE STRUGGLE BETWEEN HIS MOTHER AND ME...

...MAYBE LEAVING HIM TO DIE WOULD HAVE BEEN KINDER.

DON'T BE FOOLISH, TRENIN--

NO MATTER WHAT TROUBLE EXISTS BETWEEN HIS MOTHER AND YOU, DEATH IS NEVER A BETTER ANSWER.

"TRENIN, I **TRUST** YOU. DO WHAT YOU MUST, BUT **DO** THINK OF THE BOY. WHATEVER THIS TROUBLE IS, **END** IT."

COME, SEAHN...

...LET'S GO **HUNTING.**